Little Red
Riding Hood

Illustrated by Diana Mayo

Little Red Riding Hood lived with her mother and father in a house in the forest.

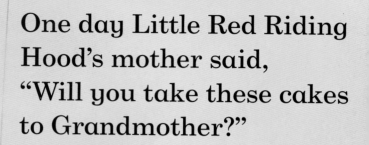

One day Little Red Riding Hood's mother said, "Will you take these cakes to Grandmother?"

"Yes," said Little Red Riding Hood, and off she went.

8

9

Grandmother's house was on the other side of the forest. And in the forest lived a wolf.

11

When the wolf saw Little
Red Riding Hood he said,
"I will eat her all up!"
And off he ran.

Little Red Riding Hood knocked on her grandmother's door.

"Come in," said a funny voice.

Little Red Riding Hood looked at her grandmother.

"Come closer, my dear," said the funny voice.

"Oh, Grandmother," said Little Red Riding Hood. "What big ears you have!"

"All the better to hear you with, my dear," said the funny voice. "Come closer."

19

"Oh, Grandmother," said
Little Red Riding Hood.
"What big eyes you have!"

"All the better to see
you with, my dear,"
said the funny voice.
"Come closer."

"Oh, Grandmother," said
Little Red Riding Hood.
"What big teeth you have!"

"All the better to eat you
with!" cried the wolf.

23

The wolf jumped up
and chased Little Red
Riding Hood round and
round the house.

"Help!" cried Little Red
Riding Hood.

Little Red Riding Hood's
father was in the forest.

He ran to Grandmother's
door with his big axe.

The wolf jumped up
when he saw the axe.

Then he ran and ran
and was never seen
in the forest again.

29

How much do you remember about the story of Little Red Riding Hood? Answer these questions and find out!

- Where is Little Red Riding Hood going?

- Who sees her in the forest?

- Who is the wolf pretending to be?

- Who rescues Little Red Riding Hood and Grandmother?